# I-SPY

# TRUCKS
## & TRUCKING

**This book belongs to:**

I began this book on: (DATE)

I made my first I-Spy on: (DATE)

I sent off for my badge on: (DATE)

To get you started on the 1000 points you need for a badge, here are a few easy spots you can make now.

Which two sorts of drinks are carried by the Iveco-Ford Cargo in the 'Types of Truck' section?
**5 points for a right answer**

In the 'Foreign Trucks' section, how many are powered by Renault?
**5 points for a right answer**

What kind of hazardous load is shown on the 'Hazchem' board in the 'Truck Features' section?
**5 points for a right answer**

The Racing car transporter in the 'Specialized Trucks' section is carrying which Formula 1 team?
**5 points for a right answer**

*Answers on page 48*

## Bedford TL Four Wheeler

Bedford is a famous make once built in Dunstable. Over 3,000,000 were built. The factory closed in 1992 but now small numbers are built in Cambridge by Marshall SPV. They have Perkins engines. Between 1987 and 1992 Bedfords were badged with a different name. What was it?

*I-Spy for 10 – double with answer*

## DAF 95XF Artic.

DAF Trucks originate from Holland but have been sold in Britain for more than twenty-five years. Some are badged 'Leyland DAF' since Leyland and DAF merged in 1987. This 95XF has a 430 bhp diesel engine.

*I-Spy for 5*

### ERF EC10 Rigid Eight-wheeler

ERF are the initials of Edwin Richard Foden. Edwin and his brother William built Foden trucks. Then, in 1933, Edwin formed his own company called 'ERF'. ERF was the last big British truck manufacturer until taken over by Western Star of Canada in 1996. This eight-wheeler has a flat body.

*I-Spy for 25*

### ERF EC11 Artic

ERF 'EC' trucks are fitted with 'SP' cabs and have American engines built by Cummins, Caterpillar, and Detroit Diesel. This is an EC11 with a Cummins engine and has a curtain-sided trailer. What does 'SP' stand for?

*I-Spy for 5*
*Double with answer*

### Foden 3000 Rigid Eight-wheeler

This Foden eight-wheeled tanker is in the colours of Shell UK, the famous petrol company, and is used to distribute fuel. When fully loaded, eight-wheelers can weigh up to 32 tonnes.

*I-Spy for 15*

**Foden Alpha 3000 Artic.**
Foden is one of the oldest names, and dates back to 1856. Foden once built steam lorries. Since 1980 it has been owned by the American company Paccar which also owns Leyland DAF. Some Fodens now have Leyland DAF cabs but have their own design of front grille as on this artic. used to carry cement.
*I-Spy for 5*

**Iveco-Ford Cargo Four-wheeler**
This 7.5 tonne gross van is used to deliver cider. It has a sleeper cab and curtain-sided body – the curtains can be slid back to reach the load. Ford Trucks were merged with Iveco (**I**ndustrial **Ve**hicle **Co**rporation of Europe) in 1987 and became Iveco-Ford Trucks.
*I-Spy for 5*

**Isuzu Light Truck**
Light trucks are popular for small loads in and around town. Isuzus originate from Japan but some were assembled in Britain by Leyland Trucks and more recently by ERF.
*I-Spy for 10*

**Iveco-Ford Eurotech Artic.**
Iveco-Ford's 38 tonne artic. is available with engines from 300 to 420 bhp. It is seen here in Elddis colours. 'Elddis' is 'Siddle' back to front. 'Siddle' Cook was a well-known haulier in Consett, Co. Durham years ago, and Elddis Transport is the present-day company formed by Siddle's sons.
*I-Spy for 5*

**Leyland DAF 55 Four-wheeler**
With a 'gross' weight of 17 tonnes, this four-wheeler has a refrigerated body to keep its load of milk fresh. 'Gross' weight is the total weight of the truck with a full load.
*I-Spy for 15*

5

**Leyland DAF 85 Drawbar**
For extra load capacity, powerful trucks can be coupled to trailers forming 'drawbar outfits'. These can weigh up to 38 tonnes and measure 18.35 metres long. Williams Distribution has a large fleet and originates from North Wales.
*I-Spy for 10*

**MAN L2000 Four-wheeler.**
Not all loads demand big trucks. This MAN carries just 5 tonnes and is powered by a 155 bhp diesel engine. MAN is a German manufacturer.
*I-Spy for 10*

**MAN Rigid Eight-wheeler**
Most eight-wheeled rigids are fitted with tipper bodies but this one has a curtain-sided body for carrying paper. Can you I-Spy an eight-wheeler like this one?
*I-Spy for 25*

## MAN F2000 Artic.

MANs are very popular as articulated trucks. Here is a smart example about to deliver a load of bricks to a building site in Somerset. It has a self-loading crane so that the driver can unload it all alone.
*I-Spy for 5*

## Mercedes Benz Atego Four-wheeler

Introduced in 1998, this is one of the most advanced medium-weight trucks. It has disc brakes and a 150 bhp 4-cylinder diesel. There are larger Ategos up to 18 tonnes gross as well as six- and eight-wheelers up to 32 tonnes. This one weighs 7.5 tonnes gross and is used for express deliveries.
*I-Spy for 5*

## Mercedes Benz Actros Artic.

For heavy loads over long distances the powerful Actros is available as an artic. (seen here) or as a drawbar outfit, with engines from 313 bhp to 570 bhp, and gross weights up to 41 tonnes. This nicely liveried artic. has a 394 bhp V-6 engine.
*I-Spy for 5*

### Renault Midliner Four-wheeler

Designed to carry 4 to 5 tonnes, the Midliner is well suited to shop deliveries in busy towns. This one is part of the large Bibby Distribution fleet and delivers goods for Boots the Chemists.
*I-Spy for* **10**

### Renault Magnum Artic.

The Magnum has a very tall cab providing lots of space and comfort. Usually they are seen coupled to van trailers but this one has a flat trailer, emphasizing the height of the cab. Artics like this with six axles can weigh up to 41 tonnes gross.
*I-Spy for* **10**

### Scania 94D Four-wheeler

A smart colour scheme in the traditional style makes this 17-tonne gvw refrigerated boxvan stand out. The 'fridge' body keeps foodstuffs and vegetables fresh on their way to the super-market.

*I-Spy for* **15**

### Scania 114C Rigid Eight–wheeler.

Heavy duty tippers like this 32-tonne gvw Scania are used to transport earth and building materials to and from construction sites.

*I-Spy for* **10**

### Scania 124L Artic.

This smart, six-axle artic. offers the driver a high degree of comfort for long-distance journeys. In which country are Scania trucks built?

*I-Spy for* **5**
*Double with answer*

9

### Seddon-Atkinson Strato 325 Rigid Eight-wheeler

With a gvw of 32 tonnes, this Strato is Seddon-Atkinson's largest rigid. Like most 'eight-wheelers', it actually has twelve wheels but the rear wheels are 'twinned', each pair counting as one wide wheel.
*I-Spy for* **25**

### Seddon-Atkinson Strato 210 Four-wheeler

Seddon-Atkinsons are built in Oldham in Lancashire. Seddon was formed in 1938 and took over Atkinson Vehicles of Preston in 1970. Seddon-Atkinson is now owned by Iveco, so the two makes have similarities in their cab designs.
*I-Spy for* **15**

### Volvo FL6
### Four-wheeler
The FL6 ranges from 11 tonnes gvw up to 17 tonnes gvw. All have 6-litre turbo-charged diesel engines. Volvos originate from Sweden but also have an assembly plant in Scotland.
*I-Spy for 5*

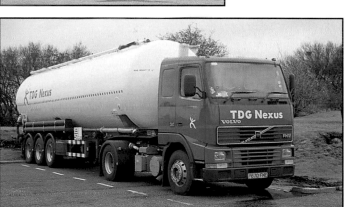

**Volvo FH12 Artic.**
Since they were first sold in Britain in 1967, Volvos have become one of the most popular makes, and the FH is their 'top-of-the-range' model for long-distance hauls at up to 41 tonnes. Which Swedish city is the home of Volvo Trucks?

*I-Spy for 5 – double with answer*

**Wincanton Logistics** is one of the largest distribution companies in the UK, with over 4000 vehicles. Its origins date back to 1925. Its headquarters are in Somerset but it has a large number of depots located throughout the country. Watch out for the large 'W' logo.
*I-Spy for 5*

With around 2000 vehicles based in the UK, **TNT Logistics** is very well known. TNT stands for Thomas Nationwide Transport. The company originated in Australia. In 1998 this smart new livery was introduced.
*I-Spy for 10*

In their eye-catching green, red, and white livery, **Eddie Stobart**'s trucks are instantly recognizable and widely admired. They can be spotted all over the UK. The famous company has nearly 800 trucks and nineteen depots. All the trucks are named. This Volvo FH is named 'Chelsea'.
*I-Spy for* **5**

One of Britain's best-known flour millers is **Rank Hovis** whose large fleet of tankers delivers bulk flour to customers throughout the UK. This is an Iveco Ford Eurotech.
*I-Spy for* **10**

Worldwide parcel deliveries are undertaken by **United Parcel Services**. This Leyland DAF 95 artic. is painted in UPS 'Haulfast' livery and is used on long-distance express haulage.
*I-Spy for 10*

**Argos** shops are a familiar sight in most major towns and cities. A large fleet of trucks, including this Scania 94L drawbar outfit, is used to keep hundreds of products supplied to their busy shops.
*I-Spy for 5*

**T. Brady & Son** is an old established road transport company with its headquarters in Barrow-in-Furness. With about 125 trucks and over 300 trailers, their famous red, white, and blue livery can be spotted along most of our motorways.
*I-Spy for 10*

This nicely painted Scania 114L artic. appears in **Knauf**'s blue and white livery. It carries plasterboard for the building industry.
*I-Spy for 20*

**BRS** stands for 'British Road Services'. Once upon a time, fifty years ago, the bulk of long-distance transport in the UK was carried out by BRS. BRS is now a large truck-rental fleet owned by Volvo Trucks.
*I-Spy for 5*

Transporting all kinds of bulk liquids needs special tankers like this MAN F2000 artic. of **Norman Lewis**, a well-known international fleet from Huddersfield in Yorkshire.
*I-Spy for 15*

**Tibbett & Britten** is a very large company with thousands of trucks operating throughout Europe and many other countries. One of its many UK customers is B & Q Warehouse, the famous DIY stores. What does DIY stand for?

*I-Spy for* **5**
*Double with answer*

**James Irlam** began as a family business fifty years ago in Cheshire, and has developed into a large logistics company with 250 tractors and 400 trailers used mainly for food and drinks distribution.
*I-Spy for* **5**

Since it was established in 1953, South Wales-based **John Raymond Transport** has grown into a major company with 200 tractor units and over 600 trailers. This smart Volvo FL10 artic. carries Rockwool Insulation products.
*I-Spy for* **10**

**Canute**'s bright yellow trucks stand out and can easily be I-Spied as they travel the motorways with general cargoes including building materials.
*I-Spy for 5*

**BOC Distribution Services** specializes in the distribution of chilled foods to well-known super-markets in the UK. The company has around 1000 trucks typified by this ERF EC12 artic. which is powered by natural gas for a cleaner environment.
*I-Spy for 10*

# FAMOUS FLEETS

This smart Renault Premium artic. is one of a large fleet operated by **City Transport**. It is pulling a tri-axle curtain-sided trailer.
*I-Spy for 5*

Part of a well-known fleet owned by **Richard Read** from Longhope in Gloucestershire, this colourful ERF EC10 artic. is used for general haulage.
*I-Spy for 15*

From its headquarters in Scotland, **Russell Transport** operates 160 tractors and over 450 trailers. The striking pale-lilac livery makes them easy to spot.
*I-Spy for 15*

**TDG Linkman** is a famous bulk-liquid tanker fleet and is part of the large Transport Development Group plc. The group has around 1800 tractors and 3000 trailers, making it one of the largest in the UK. Its trademark is a juggler which appears on all TDG trucks.
*I-Spy for 5*

**Gregory Distribution**'s smart fleet of brown artics, mostly Mercedes Benz and Scanias, can be seen carrying fresh milk, foodstuffs, and confectionery mainly throughout the south-west of England.
*I-Spy for 20*

Based at Guyhirn in the fenlands of East Anglia, **Ken Thomas** has a large fleet of artics which stand out by virtue of their attractive traditional-style colour scheme.
*I-Spy for 15*

# FAMOUS FLEETS

**Dodd's Transport** is an old established company based at Southall in Middlesex. Many of its current fleet carry paper, and bear the 'UK Paper' logo as seen on this Volvo FH tractor unit.

*I-Spy for 10*

Delivering supplies of food and other goods to the many **Kwiksave** supermarkets is a fleet of modern artics like this Scania 114L.

*I-Spy for 5*

**P&O Roadtanks** is part of the large P&O Trans European Group which has depots throughout the UK and Europe. This smart Mercedes Benz Actros tanker carries chemicals. What does 'P&O' stand for?

*I-Spy for 5*
*Double with answer*

This ERF EC10, painted in the well-known **Roadways** livery, is hauling a 40-foot or '12-metre' ISO container to a container port where it will be transferred on to a ship. Containers are carried on 'skeletal' trailers – a simple open framework – and are attached by twist-locks at each corner.

*I Spy for* **10**

Pausing at a motorway services is this fine example of a long-distance artic. from the large **Currie Transport** fleet from Dumfries in Scotland. It is a 430 bhp DAF 95XF.
*I-Spy for* **10**

# FAMOUS FLEETS

In its smart red livery, this Leyland DAF 85 artic. of **Swift Transport Services** from Northampton has a large-volume trailer for carrying light, bulky cargoes.
*I-Spy for 5*

**J. H. Harding & Sons** of Frome in Somerset specializes in temperature-controlled transport of foodstuffs. This Scania 113M has a refrigerated van trailer.
*I-Spy for 15*

Bringing breakfast cereal to the shops requires a large fleet of trucks. This bright yellow Scania 113M artic. distributes **Weetabix** from the famous company's factory at Burton Latimer, Northamptonshire.
*I-Spy for 5*

**Securicor Omega Logistics** have over 500 tractor units and 860 trailers in this eye-catching light-blue livery. This Renault Premium is hauling a short skeletal trailer with a 6-metre ISO container.
*I-Spy for 5*

Based at Leeds in South Yorkshire, **MacFarlane Transport** was established in 1978, and has grown into a large distribution company with seventy tractor units and 110 trailers, all finished in this distinctive green and yellow livery.
*I-Spy for 10*

Wimblington, near March in Cambridgeshire, is the home base of this attractive Volvo FL10 artic., one of a large fleet operated by **Knowles Transport**.
*I-Spy for 15*

As part of the employee-owned National Freight Consortium plc, **Exel Logistics** is the UK's largest contract distribution company with a fleet of 6100 vehicles and 8300 trailers, plus a further 3600 in overseas' locations.
*I-Spy for 5*

**NFT Distribution**, a subsidiary of Northern Foods, specializes in chilled food distribution. It has 230 artics based at three main depots.
*I-Spy for 5*

The **Shore Porters Society**, based in Aberdeen, is the oldest transport company in the world, and dates back 500 years. Originally, loads would have been carried locally by porters or on packhorses.
*I-Spy for 20*

**Tesco** is one of the country's best-known supermarkets, with stores throughout the UK. Keeping the shelves filled with hundreds of different products is a large fleet of artics like this Scania 94D.
*I-Spy for 5*

One of Britain's biggest truck fleets, **Hays Distribution** has 1500 trucks and 2000 trailers. Its headquarters is in Milton Keynes but Hays's trucks can be seen all over the country.
*I-Spy for 5*

Established in 1987, **Lynx Express** is a leading parcels carrier incorporating Red Star parcel services. All Lynx trucks appear in this distinctive black livery with a red band.
*I-Spy for 5*

**Willi Betz** is a familiar name on British roads even though the trucks come from near Stuttgart in Germany. This Mercedes Benz Actros is coupled to a 'tilt' trailer for international transport.
*I-Spy for 5*

Regular visitors to the UK are the smart orange and cream trucks of **J. Heebink bv.** of Veenendaal in the Netherlands. This is a 400 bhp Scania 124L.
*I-Spy for 10*

From France comes this special Renault 340 with a show trailer all painted up in the bright yellow and blue livery of the famous **Michelin Tyre Company**.
*I-Spy for 15*

# OVERSEAS' TRUCKS

Although this Renault Premium artic. bears the familiar **TDG** (Transport Development Group) logo, it belongs to one of the group's European companies, Innocenti-Royer, and has French number plates.
*I-Spy for 5*

**José Carrillo** has a large fleet of trucks in Spain and has been operating a regular service to the UK since the 1970s. This powerful Renault Magnum is ideal for such long hauls.
*I-Spy for 5*

**Visbeen Transport** runs this 480 bhp DAF 95XF artic. between De Lier in Holland and the United Kingdom. The company has chosen to use a slogan in English 'Because we care' for the front of the cab.
*I-Spy for 10*

This attractive Iveco Eurostar artic. of Udo Hatzl hauls a tilt trailer in the orange livery of **Gebrüder Weiss** between Austria and Britain.
*I-Spy for 15*

The striking metallic silver and blue livery of **H. J. van Bentum** of Woudenberg in the Netherlands can be seen every day on Britain's motorways. This is a Scania 124L artic. tanker.
*I-Spy for 5*

# OVERSEAS' TRUCKS

See if you can I-Spy the big 'G', which stands for '**Giraud**', a famous French transport company. Blue, white, and red are the colours of the French national flag. What is the flag called?

*I-Spy for **5** – double with answer*

**Norbert Dentressangle** of France is one of the largest and best-known transport companies. Its trucks can be seen all over Europe, including the United Kingdom. This smart Renault Premium is seen on the M1 motorway.

*I-Spy for **5***

From distant Warsaw in Poland, this Volvo FH12 is in the yellow livery of **Pekaes Transport**. Its heavy duty 'tilt' trailer can be sealed to avoid delays at customs as it crosses international borders.
*I-Spy for* **10**

Liaz trucks are built in the Czech Republic, and **CSAD** is the Czech state transport company. Their trucks can be seen regularly throughout Britain and Europe.
*I-Spy for* **10**

As the name suggests, **Hungarocamion** is the Hungarian state transport company. The trucks from this vast fleet travel all over Europe. This DAF 95 from their Budapest base is hauling a refrigerated trailer.
*I-Spy for* **5**

**Timber**
Hauling round timber out of the forests is tough work. This 420 bhp Volvo FH12 drawbar outfit has a heavy duty crane to lift the logs on and off.
*I-Spy for 15*

**Building materials**
Delivering building materials is made quick and easy by truck-mounted self-loading cranes as fitted to this Scania 94C eight-wheeler loaded with sand in large 'tote' bags.
*I-Spy for 10*

## Sheeted load

Traditional-style British trucks had platform or 'flat' trailers, and loads had to be sheeted and securely roped like this load of waste paper. Such trailers are not as common now as they were years ago.

*I-Spy for 15*

## Earth

Excavating a building site calls for rugged eight-wheeled tippers. This Renault is being loaded by a tracked loading shovel and can carry over 20 tonnes in one load.

*I-Spy for 5*

**Cars**
As many as ten cars or light vans can be carried in one load by modern transporters so that they can arrive at the dealers in perfect condition.
*I-Spy for 5*

**Chemicals**
Drivers of chemical tankers are specially trained in safety procedures, and such tankers have 'Hazchem' signs to identify the type of chemicals that are being carried.
*I-Spy for 10*

**Palletized goods**
Most types of load are carried in 'curtain-sided' trailers so that fork-lift trucks can gain easy access for loading and unloading. Loads are 'palletized' on wooden pallets for ease of handling.
*I-Spy for 5*

**Sugar beet**
During autumn and winter, thousands of tons of sugar beet are transported from farms to the sugar refineries. Here an articulated bulk tipper discharges its load on the stock-pile at a refinery.
*I-Spy for 15*

**Building blocks**
Loading concrete building blocks is speeded up by using fork-lift trucks with specially designed 'grippers'. This Foden also has its own crane for unloading at the building site
*I-Spy for 10*

**Glass**
This unusual-looking trailer is designed to carry large sheets of glass, and has special equipment to load and unload the heavy glass.
*I-Spy for 20*

## Fuel

Petrol and diesel fuel is delivered to filling stations and other customers in bulk tankers which are loaded at storage depots. Special safety precautions are taken to eliminate the risk of fire.
*I-Spy for 10*

## Livestock

Up to forty cattle or 450 sheep can be transported in safety using specially designed livestock trailers like this one seen coupled to an ERF EC14 tractor unit.
*I-Spy for 10*

## Steel

Modern steel carriers have sliding canopies to allow overhead loading by crane and to protect the steel from the weather. The canopies can easily be opened and closed by one person because they are on rollers.

*I-Spy for 10*

## Skip

For the easy movement of rubbish and waste materials, there are special self-loading 'skip wagons'. A full skip is picked up by the hydraulic lift and an empty one can be left for the customer.

*I-Spy for 5*

## Milk

Fresh milk from farms is collected in small tankers that can pass through narrow farm gateways easily. The milk is then taken to dairies and bottling plants.

*I-Spy for 5*

### Cab roof deflector
Roof deflectors not only add style but cut down wind resistance by deflecting air upwards over the trailer. This can save fuel on long journeys because the engine does not have to work so hard.
*I-Spy for* **5**

### Air horns
Air-operated horns make a loud noise and can be used to warn other road users. On some busy European roads drivers use them more frequently than in the United Kingdom.
*I-Spy for* **15**

### Tilt cab
Modern trucks have cabs that tilt forwards so that mechanics can work on the engines.
*I-Spy for* **20**

### Vertical exhaust
Shiny, vertical exhaust stacks not only look smart but blow exhaust gases upwards, away from pedestrians.
*I-Spy for 15*

### Rear marker
On trucks weighing more than 7.5 tonnes gvw, reflective rear markers are required by law to reflect the headlights of following traffic at night.
*I-Spy for 5*

### Custom paint
Proud drivers like to make their trucks stand out by decorating them with unique custom paint jobs.
*I-Spy for 20*

**Hazchem warning**
'Hazchem' boards are fitted to trucks carrying hazardous loads, and a code identifies the goods being carried.
*I-Spy for 15*

**Fifth-wheel coupling**
To attach trailers securely to tractor units a strong coupling is used. This is called a 'fifth-wheel' coupling and can be seen best on a tractor running 'solo'. What does solo mean?

*I-Spy for 15*
Double with answer

**Lift axle**
Some heavy trucks have lift-up axles to save on tyre wear when running unladen.
*I-Spy for 10*

### Trailer airlines
To operate the trailer brakes and lights, artics and drawbar outfits have colour-coded airlines and cables. They are sometimes called 'suzies'. They are 'coiled' so that they can stretch when cornering.
*I-Spy for 5*

### Cab-top sleeper
Where maximum load space is required, the sleeping quarters for the driver are mounted on top of the cab and are entered through an aperture in the cab roof.
*I-Spy for 15*

### Bulk-powder tanker
Cement and other powders can be transported in bulk using special trailers like this Metalair-Feldbinder tanker. It can carry up to 30 tonnes, and the load is 'blown' out using low-pressure air.
*I-Spy for 10*

# SPECIALIZED TRUCKS

### Ridgeback
For delivering soft drinks there are special trucks with very low load platforms. Known as 'Ridgebacks', they have a specially shaped chassis with a single central frame.
*I-Spy for 15*

### Fire appliance
Always ready to turn out quickly, fire appliances save lives in emergencies such as house fires and road accidents. Fire appliances have flashing beacons. What colour are they?

*I-Spy for 15*
*Double with answer*

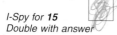

### Recovery truck
Heavy recovery trucks come in all shapes and sizes. This eight-wheeled monster can lift-tow a fully loaded truck to safety in the event of a breakdown or an accident.
*I-Spy for 20*

**Heavy indivisible load**
The largest of all trucks can weigh over 500 tons, and journeys have to be planned well in advance. Such massive outfits, up to 100 metres in length, are escorted by police to warn other road users.
*I-Spy for* **25**

**Readymix truck**
To speed up construction of buildings special 'Readymix' trucks are used to deliver fresh concrete which is poured directly on to the site.
*I-Spy for* **10**

**Mobile crane**
Mobile cranes capable of lifting up to 100 tonnes are used in large construction projects. They have many axles to spread the load evenly on the road surface when travelling from site to site.
*I-Spy for 20*

**Racing truck**
Some trucks are built purely for truck racing and are not used to pull trailers at all. They are very fast and have special internal 'roll-cages' to protect the racing driver in the event of a roll-over.
*I-Spy for 25*

**Refuse collector**
Refuse-collection trucks have grown larger and larger in recent years to cope with the increasing amounts of domestic waste. This monster weighs 30 tonnes when fully laden.
*I-Spy for 10*

### Racing car transporter
Racing car transporters are always painted in smart liveries, and usually advertise the team sponsor's name. They travel all over the world to Formula 1 Grand Prix events.

*I-Spy for* **25**

### Dump truck
You will sometimes I-Spy these unusual-looking dump trucks hauling earth and rock on large construction sites. They steer by hinging in the middle.

*I-Spy for* **20**

# SPECIALIZED TRUCKS

**Snow plough**
Keeping the roads clear in treacherous winter snow is important for the safety of motorists. This Seddon Atkinson also spreads grit and rock salt to dissolve ice.
*I-Spy for 20*

**Army truck**
Military trucks are very tough and are designed to travel over rough, unmade tracks as well as on normal roads. They are often driven on all wheels.
*I-Spy for 15*

**Low loader**
For transporting heavy machines, special trailers called 'low loaders' are used. The machine can be driven on and steered into position before being securely chained down for safety.
*I-Spy for 10*

## Mobile advertising truck

Some trucks are fitted with large 'hoardings' and are used purely to advertise products or events. They are sometimes parked in strategic positions or can be driven around for maximum publicity.

*I-Spy for 15*

## Hydraulic platform

Reaching high buildings for maintenance is made possible with the use of special hydraulically operated platform hoists. They are sometimes called 'cherry pickers'.

*I-Spy for 10*

# INDEX

**Answers**

Title page: Cider and perry; 5; Flammable liquid; Williams Bedford; AWD ERF EC; Steel; Plastic; Scania artic; Sweden Volvo FH; snow plough; It Yourself; Britain/B&Q; Do Peninsular & Oriental; Giraud; Tricolour Fifth wheel; On its own (without trailer); Fire appliance; Blue

© I-Spy Limited 1999

ISBN 1 85671 209 5

Michelin Tyre Public Limited Company
Edward Hyde Building, 38 Clarendon Road, Watford, Herts WD1 1SX

MICHELIN and the Michelin Man are Registered Trademarks of Michelin

A CIP record for this title is available from the British Library.

Edited by Neil Curtis. Designed by Richard Garratt.

The Publisher gratefully acknowledges the contribution of Peter J. Davies who provided the majority of the photographs in this book, and who also compiled the text. Additional photographs have been supplied by BOC and TNT.

Colour reproduction by Anglia Colour Ltd.

Printed in Spain by Graficromo SA.